TAKE THE LEAD
PIANO

Bumper Book

Editorial, production and recording: Artemis Music Limited (www.artemismusic.com) • Published 2005

Angels

Demonstration: CD1
Backing: CD2

Words and Music by Robert Williams
and Guy Chambers

Rather slow

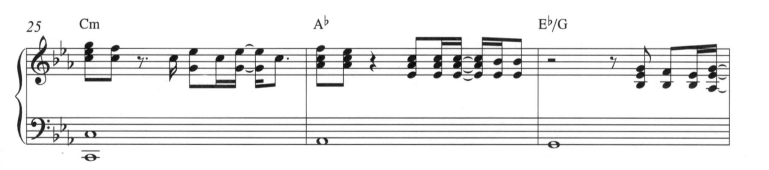

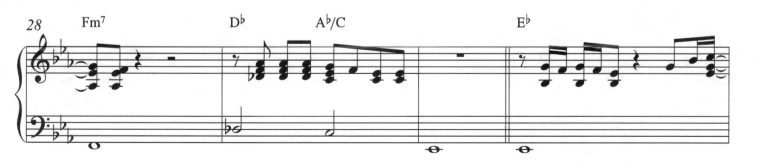

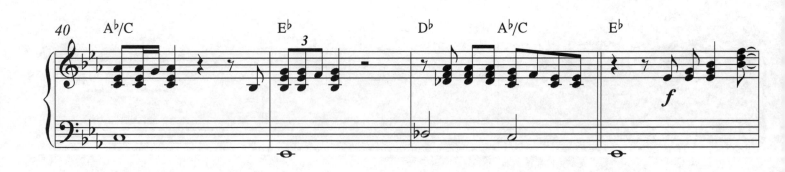

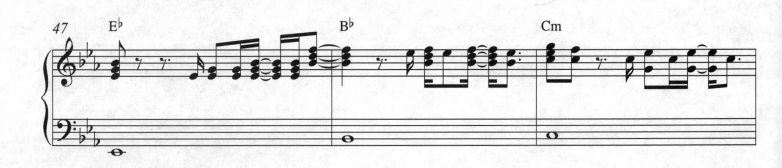

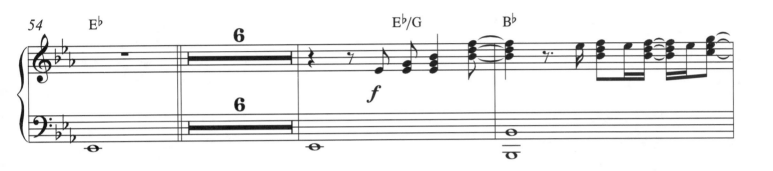

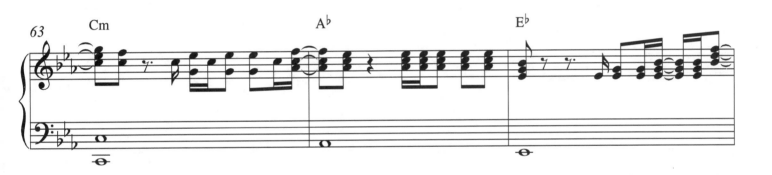

Blueberry Hill

Words and Music by Al Lewis,
Vincent Rose and Larry Stock

Demonstration: CD1
Backing: CD2

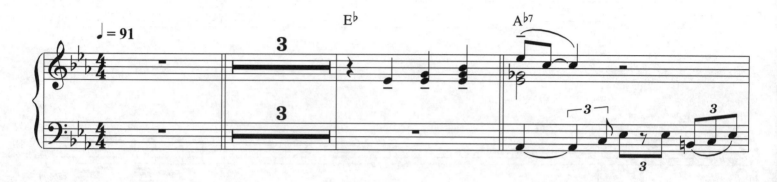

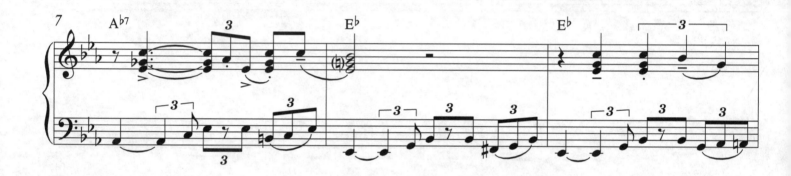

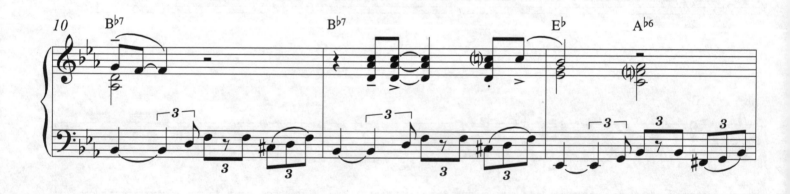

© 1940 Chappell & Co Ltd, USA
Warner/Chappell Music Ltd, London W6 8BS and Redwood Music Ltd, London NW1 8BD

Careless Whisper

Words and Music by George Michael
and Andrew Ridgeley

Demonstration: CD1
Backing: CD2

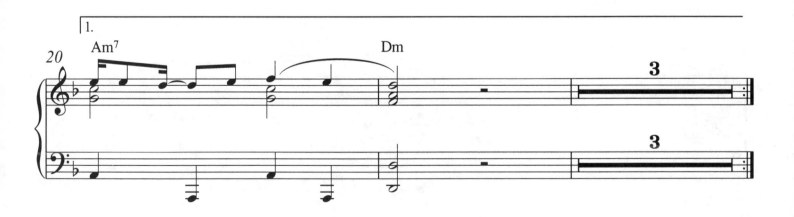

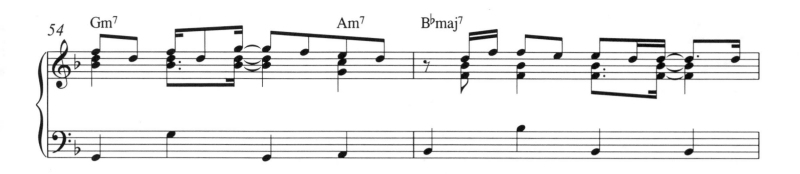

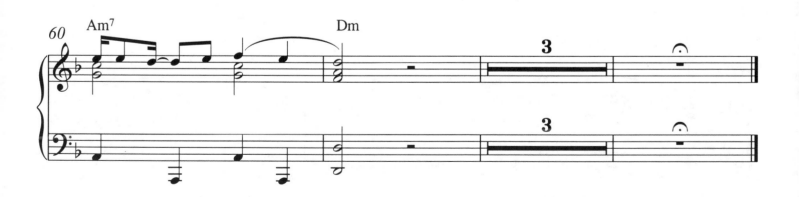

Dance Of The Sugar Plum Fairy

Music by Pyotr Ilych Tchaikovsky

Demonstration: CD1
Backing: CD2

Come Away With Me

Words and Music by Norah Jones

Demonstration: CD1
Backing: CD2

Slow waltz tempo

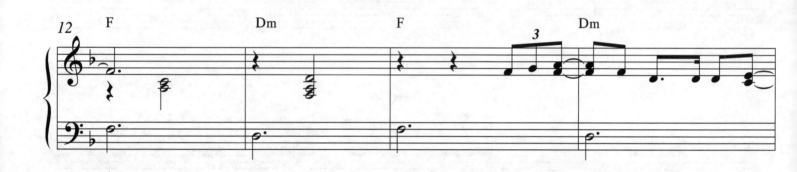

Everybody Needs Somebody To Love

Words and Music by Bert Burns,
Solomon Burke and Jerry Wexler

Demonstration: CD1
Backing: CD2

Fascinating Rhythm

Music and Lyrics by George Gershwin
and Ira Gershwin

Demonstration: CD1
Backing: CD2

In The Mood

Words by Andy Razaf
Music by Joe Garland

Demonstration: CD1
Backing: CD2

Bright swing

I'll Be There For You

Words and Music by
Phil Solem, Marta Kauffman, David Crane,
Michael Skloff, Allee Willis and Danny Wilde

Demonstration: CD1
Backing: CD2

⊕ CODA

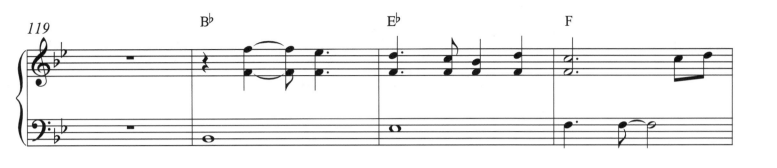

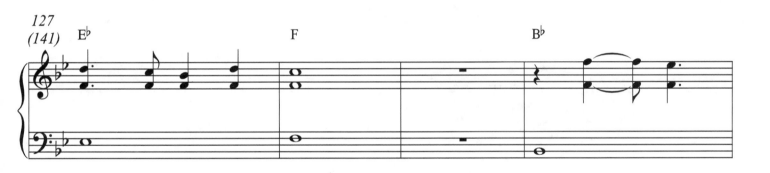

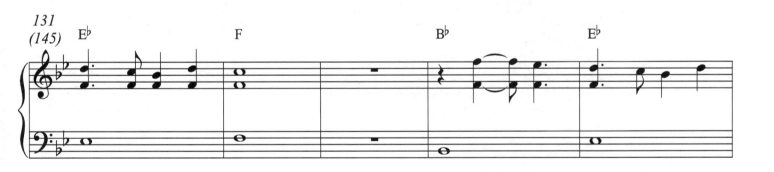

La Bamba

Traditional
Arranged by Ritchie Valens

Demonstration: CD1
Backing: CD2

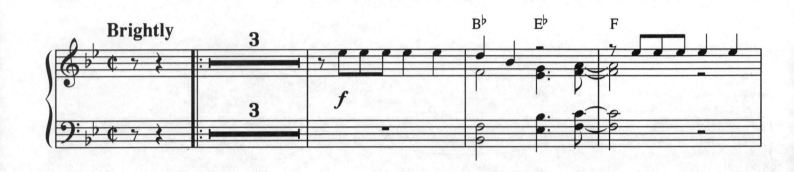

Guantanamera

Words and Music by Diaz Fernandez

Demonstration: CD1
Backing: CD2

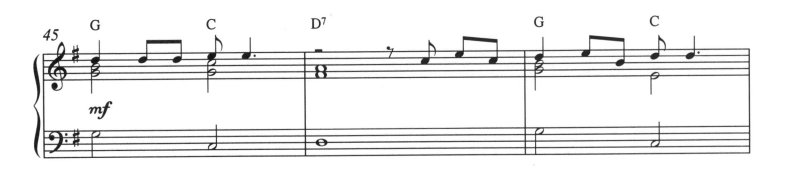

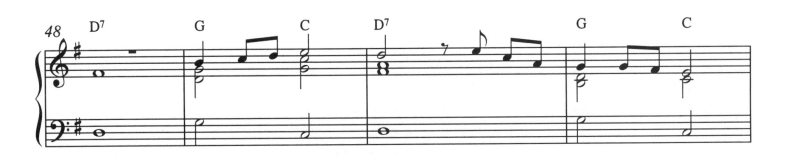

My Heart Will Go On

Words by Will Jennings
Music by James Horner

Demonstration: CD1
Backing: CD2

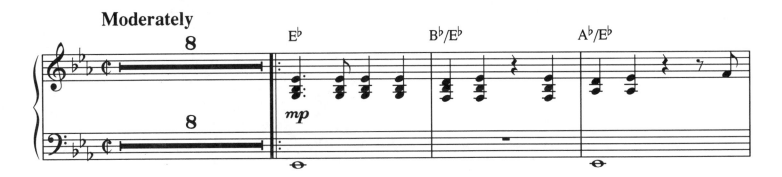

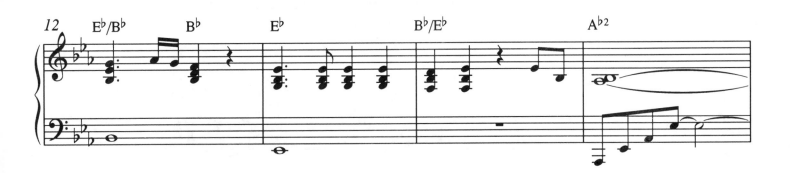

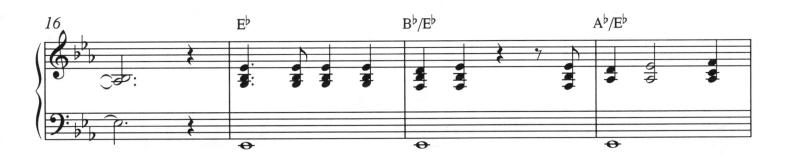

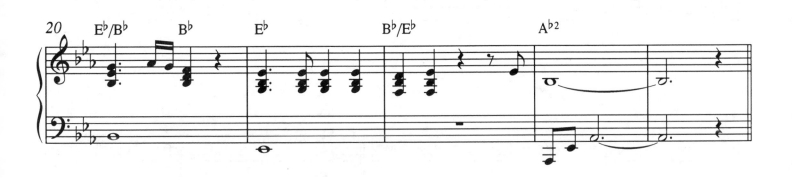

Over The Rainbow

Words by E Y Harburg
Music by Harold Arlen

Demonstration: CD1
Backing: CD2

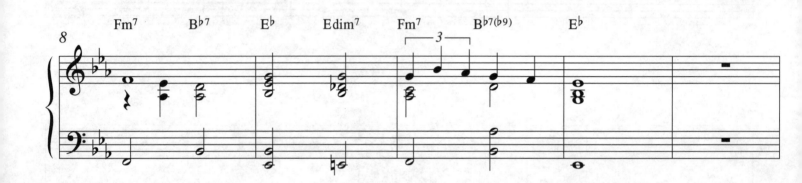

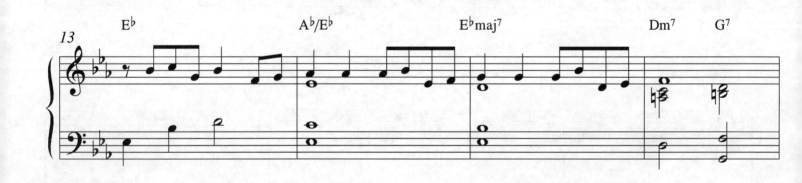

Singin' In The Rain

Words by Arthur Freed
Music by Nacio Herb Brown

Demonstration: CD1
Backing: CD2

CODA

Sound Of The Underground

Demonstration: CD1
Backing: CD2

Words and Music by Brian Higgins,
Niara Scarlett and Miranda Cooper

Driving rock tempo

Warner/Chappell Music Publishing Ltd, London W6 8BS

Summer Nights

Words and Music by Jim Jacobs
and Warren Casey

Demonstration: CD1
Backing: CD2

Summertime

(from *Porgy and Bess*®)

Demonstration: CD1
Backing: CD2

Music and Lyrics by George Gershwin,
Du Bose Heyward, Dorothy Heyward
and Ira Gershwin

Relaxed Swing

60

9/03

Star Wars (Main Theme)

Music by John Williams

Demonstration: CD1
Backing: CD2

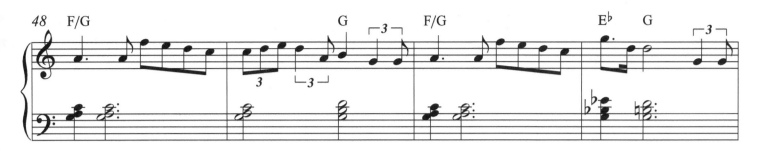

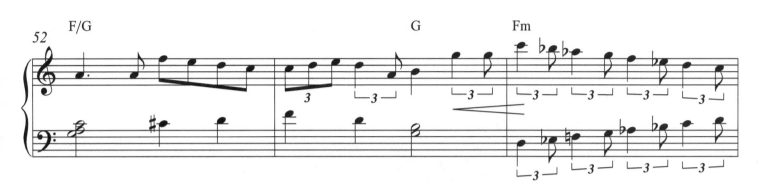

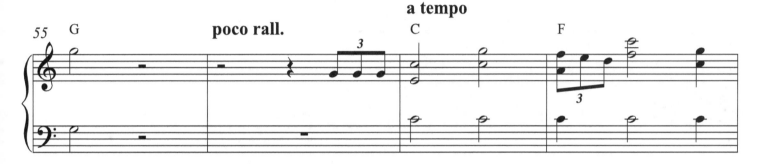

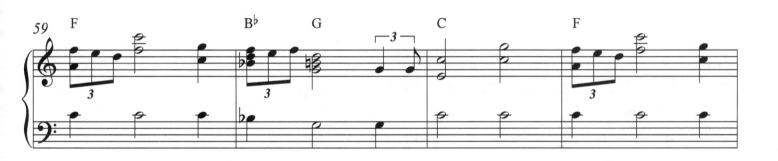

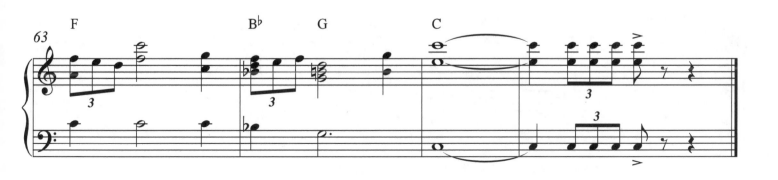

When You Say Nothing At All

Words and Music by Paul Overstreet
and Don Schlitz

Demonstration: CD1
Backing: CD2

Uptown Girl

Words and Music by Billy Joel

Demonstration: CD1
Backing: CD2

Moderate rock and roll

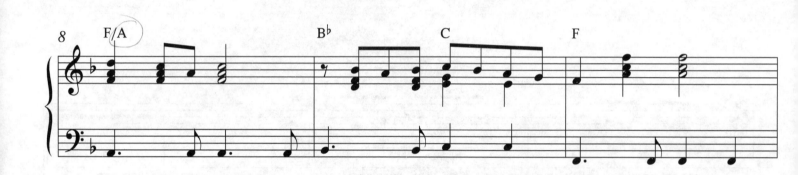

TAKE THE LEAD

PIANO *Bumper Book*

Angels (Robbie Williams)

Blueberry Hill

Careless Whisper (George Michael)

Come Away With Me (Norah Jones)

Dance Of The Sugar Plum Fairy
(Tchaikovsky)

Everybody Needs Somebody To
Love (from *The Blues Brothers*)

Fascinating Rhythm

Guantanamera

I'll Be There For You (Theme from *Friends*)

In The Mood

La Bamba

My Heart Will Go On (Celine Dion)

Over The Rainbow

Singin' In The Rain

Sound Of The Underground (Girls Aloud)

Star Wars (Main Theme)

Summer Nights (from *Grease*)

Summertime

Uptown Girl (Westlife)

When You Say Nothing At All
(Ronan Keating)

FEATURES

In The Book:

carefully selected and edited
piano arrangements

chord symbols in concert pitch

On The CDs:

- full backing tracks,
  professionally arranged
  and recorded

- full demonstration recordings
  to help you learn the songs

Take The Lead is an integrated series for Alto Saxophone, Clarinet, Flute, Recorder, Piano,
Tenor Saxophone, Trumpet and Violin. In each edition all the songs are in the same concert
pitch key, so the different instruments can play together.

All accompanying chord symbols are in concert pitch for use by piano or guitar.

FABER *ff* MUSIC

FABER MUSIC · 3 QUEEN SQUARE · LONDON
fabermusic.com

ISBN 0-571-52478-8

20 songs
£ 1.50

9 780571 524785 >